Books should be returned or renewed by the last
date above. Renew by phone **03000 41 31 31** or
online *www.kent.gov.uk/libs*

For Finian Oakleigh – A.S.

For Mum – F.L.

Published in the UK by Scholastic, 2023
1 London Bridge, London, SE1 9BG
Scholastic Ireland, 89E Lagan Road, Dublin Industrial Estate, Glasnevin, Dublin, D11 HP5F

SCHOLASTIC and associated logos are trademarks and/or
registered trademarks of Scholastic Inc.

HB ISBN 978 0702 32247 1
PB ISBN 978 0702 31041 6

A CIP catalogue record for this book is available from the British Library.

Printed in Slovakia
Paper made from wood grown in sustainable forests and other controlled sources.

1 3 5 7 9 10 8 6 4 2

www.scholastic.co.uk

5% of author royalties is being donated to The Woodland Trust.
Charity reg. number 294344 in England and Wales. SC038885 in Scotland.
www.woodlandtrust.org.uk

Amy Sparkes Fiona Lumbers

My Tree

SCHOLASTIC

My tree had been there from the beginning.

And I loved it.

If I was sad,
my tree would listen.

If I needed adventure,
my tree would play.

My family loved
my tree too.

We had marvellous fun.

And my tree
was always on my side,

in sunshine

. . . and in snow!

My tree looked after the animals.

When the leaves fell, my tree
gave the squirrels their food.

And when the flowers blossomed,
it gave the birds their home.

We travelled together for miles and miles,

across rocky plains,

and dusty roads.

We stopped a bank robbery and saved a runaway train.

When my tree held me up, I could see faraway **magical** places.

I flew with the wild geese,
and brushed the clouds with my fingertips.

A giant's tower,

an enchanted castle

and a wishing pond,

just waiting for me to explore.

But then one night it all changed.
The Dark Cloud came

and the rain poured and
poured and poured

and the wind blew . . .

and blew . . .

and blew.

It was time for my tree to go.
I would miss my friend.

Our adventures were over.

But then I saw something beautiful,
something wonderful.
A little piece of my tree.
And I knew what I could do.

I gave you a kiss, my little acorn,
and planted you well.
I watered you and took the weeds . . .

and you began to grow.

I told you stories to make you strong.
stories about runaway trains,
stories about flying

and of secret, wonderful lands
which we would see again.

And together we grew . . .

and grew . . .

and grew . . .

We are best friends,

you and me . . .

and I think we always shall be.

DISCOVER MORE ABOUT TREES

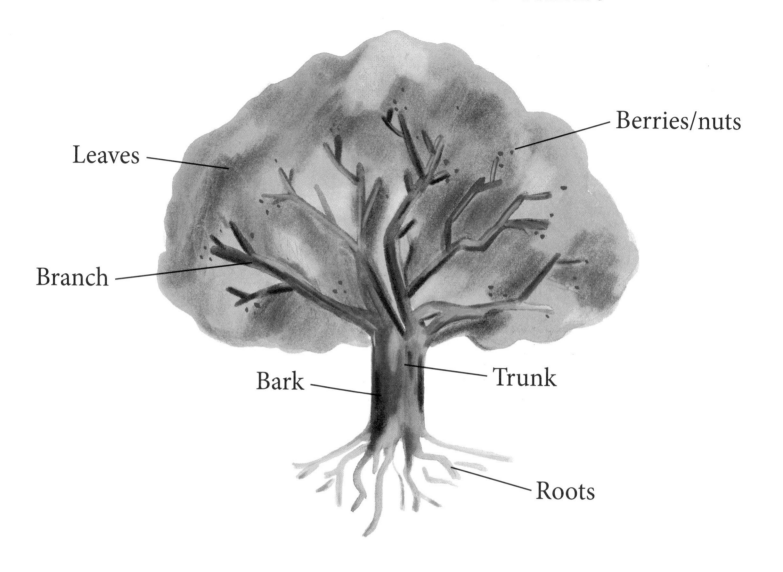

Leaves

Berries/nuts

Branch

Bark

Trunk

Roots

HOW TREES GROW

- Trees grow from seeds, although these "seeds'" can look very different!
- Trees need food and water, just like us. Using their roots, they take their water and food from the soil in the ground.
- Sunlight also helps the trees to grow.

TYPES OF TREES

There are different types of trees:

Some trees give us delicious fruit to eat, like apple trees and plum trees.

Other trees have nuts that we can eat.

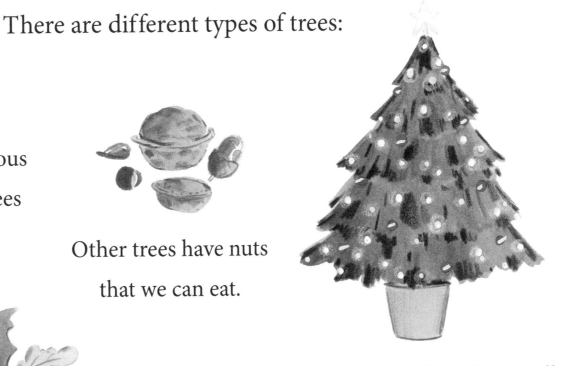

Some trees lose their leaves during the year. These are called deciduous trees.

Evergreen trees have leaves all through the year, so they are always green. We use evergreens for Christmas trees.

Some places in the world have warm summers and cold winters. After summer, the leaves of the tree change colour to red, orange, yellow and brown. Then the leaves fall from the tree as it becomes colder.

Other places in the world have wet seasons and dry seasons. The leaves use up a lot of water. So, when it is very dry, the leaves fall off to save the tree water.